SECURITY IS A THUMB AND A BLANKET

BY

CHARLES M. SCHULZ

PUBLISHED BY
DETERMINED
PRODUCTIONS, INC.
BOX 2150 SAN FRANCISCO 26,
CALIFORNIA

PROJECT DIRECTOR: CONNIE BOUCHER
ART DIRECTOR/GRAPHICS: JIM YOUNG

Security is having someone to lean on.

**Security
is knowing
you won't be
called on
to recite.**

Security is knowing who the baby sitter is.

Security
is having
your socks
match.

Security
is knowing
you still have
quite a few
years to go.

Security is owning your own home.

Security is having the music in front of you.

Security
is having
a big
brother.

Security
is sitting
in a box.

Security
is having a
good infield
behind you.

Security is having naturally curly hair.

Security
is knowing
that big dog
can't really
get out.

Security
is having
a few bones
stacked
away.

Security is holding the tickets in your hand.

Security is carrying an extra safety pin in your purse.

Security is writing down your locker combination.

Security is having some friends sleep overnight.

Security is being able to touch bottom.

Security
is giving
the mailbox
lid an
extra flip.

Security is being one of the gang.

Security
is having
someone
listen
to you.

Security
is returning
home
after a
vacation.

Security
is having
a home
town.

**Security
is getting
to the theater
before the
box office
opens.**

Security
is knowing
there's
some more
pie left.

Security
is hiding
an extra key
to the
back door.

Security
is knowing
all your
lines.

Security is a candy bar hidden in the freezer.

**Security
is hearing
your mother
in the kitchen
when you
come home
from school.**

Security is knowing you're not alone.

LITHO IN THE U.S.A.